Buckle up with this Which Way crew on your Delaware adventure:

Table of Contents

WHO is heading for the WHICH WAY HALL OF FAME?

WHAT will be in the WHICH WAY MUSEUM?

WHERE will the WHICH WAY SUPERMAX MOVIE be filmed?

Jack and Jill Underhill are twin travelers. They plan to explore the grounds of one of Delaware's most historic mansions.

STATUE STOP

The crew members begin their adventure in Wilmington, the largest city in the second-smallest state. They meet in Rodney Square. This small city park is named for one of Delaware's most famous citizens. Caesar Rodney cast an important vote that led to the adoption of the Declaration of Independence. The statue of Rodney shows him riding to Philadelphia to cast his vote.

Cara and Cliff study their Which Way map. While they plan a route through the state, you have your own Delaware work to do. Use the groups of letters in the box on page 3 to fill in the answers to the questions. Cross out each group of letters as you use them. When you are done, take a peek at the bottom of the page.

1. What is the Dutch word that means "valley of the swans"?

   Zwaanendael

2. What U.S. document is written on a stone cube in Dover?

   constitution

3. What operated on a Delaware island for 138 years?

   A lighthouse

4. What was made at Éleuthère Irénée du Pont's mill?

   gunpowder

5. Where is Fort Delaware located?

   pea patch island

6. Which river flows near Trussum Pond?

   James branch

7. What British ship sank in 1798?

   Hmb De braak

WHICH WAY USA?

STATE MAP

Don't Forget Your Map!
All the answers can be found on the *back* of your Delaware map.

LETTER BOX

HMB ~~DE~~ A ~~JA~~ ~~GUN~~ CH ~~CON~~ ~~LIG~~
PEA ~~STI~~ MES HT ~~ZWA~~ ~~POW~~ HO
UR ~~BRA~~ TU ANEN ~~TION~~ CH NCH
FO ~~USE~~ PA UND ~~TCH~~ ~~BRA~~ IS
~~DAEL~~ ER ~~AK~~ LAND ~~DER~~

Did you find all the answers?
Write the leftover letters, in order,
in the spaces below.

On page 28, cross off the

<u>church founder</u>.

Parlor Puzzle

The crew leaves Wilmington and heads for the surrounding Brandywine Valley. This area is filled with beautiful and historic sites. Cara heads straight for the Winterthur Museum. This mansion just outside Wilmington was the country home of millionaire Henry Francis du Pont. Now it is one of the most famous decorative arts museums in the country. The museum has more than 85,000 objects. They include everything from thimbles to sofas.

The crew wanders through room after room of antiques, stopping in a parlor to take a closer look at the sights. While they do, you can spot a clue. Use the letters in the parlor to complete the picture code. When you finish, let your eyes wander to the bottom of page 5.

it is not the astronomer.

Did you figure out the picture code? Now use it to cross a famous Delaware citizen off your list on page 28.

Seeing Doubles

The crew returns to the van. Jack and Jill want to get a look at another du Pont estate. Alfred I. du Pont built Nemours Mansion. It is designed to look like a magnificent French chateau. The home sits on 300 acres that include fountains, pools, statues, and beautiful gardens.

Jack and Jill take a stroll through some of the gardens. They can't believe how much there is to see. There are also some hard-to-see things along the pathway. See if you can spot the hidden items. All but one of the items are hidden twice. When you have found them, ramble over to the bottom of page 7.

Census Taker

Powder Maker

Paper Editor

Book Illustrator

Declaration Signer

Did you find the object that is hidden only once? Use the clue under it to eliminate a person on page 28.

Pass the Ps

The crew members leave the Brandywine Valley and head south. When they reach Delaware City, they catch a boat to Fort Delaware, which sits in the middle of the Delaware River on Pea Patch Island. The island was named in a funny way. According to legend, a boat full of peas sank in the river. Crates of peas washed onto the shore and pea plants grew wild on the island.

The crew lands and begins to explore the grounds of Fort Delaware. Built in 1859, the fort was a prison during the Civil War and is now part of a state park. Cy can't get Pea Patch Ps out of his mind. Help him fill in the puzzle words. Then pop over to page 9.

1. Peter _____, the pepper picker   P i p e r

2. Fluffy sleeping headrest   P i l l o w

3. Baby dog   P u p p y

4. Color of red mixed with blue   P u r p l e

5. Small pool of rainwater   P u d d l e

6. Nice-smelling liquid   P e r f u m e

7. Instrument with 88 keys   P i a n o

8. Native American gathering   P o w w o w

9. French fried or chips   P o t a t o

10. Baseball thrower   P i t c h e r

Did you polish off the puzzle? Write the circled letters from *last* to *first* here:

howard pyle

Please peruse page 28 and purge one possible person.

DAY IN BOMBAY

The crew heads south on Route 13. Cliff wants to go hiking at Bombay Hook National Wildlife Refuge. The 15,978 acres of salt marshes and swamp here are an important stopping point for migrating birds. The preserve is home to many animals, including great egrets, snow geese, white-tailed deer, and river otters.

There is a 12-mile driving loop, but Cliff wants to hit the trail on foot. He leads the crew on a path that is ideal for bird-watching. While the crew views some feathered friends, you need to observe the clues on this page. Write the correct answers *vertically* in the grid. Then check the bottom of page 11.

1. In 1963, the Delaware Turnpike opens, connecting this city to Washington, D.C.

2. Number of counties in Delaware

3. One of two towns on the Delaware-Maryland border

4. Town that is present-day site of Zwaanendael

5. Explorer of Delaware for the Netherlands

6. Delaware's state beverage

7. People who settled Zwaanendael

8. The capital of Delaware

9. The other town on the Delaware-Maryland border

Highlights
WHICH WAY
USA?

STATE MAP

Don't Forget Your Map!
Check your Delaware map for answers
to all the questions.

Did you fill in the grid?
Write the letters in the shaded boxes here:

the editor

Use this two-word clue to cross one
last Delaware citizen off the list on page 28.

Square Words

The crew returns to the road and continues south on Route 13 to Dover. Delaware's capital is the state's second-largest city. Cara drives into town to Constitution Park. In the park is a huge stone cube with a bronze quill pen beside it. This monument celebrates Delaware's special place in American history. It was the first state to ratify the U.S. Constitution.

All the words to the Constitution are written on the cube. As Jill reads the first few lines of the Constitution, Jack writes them in his electronic journal. But the Which Way kid needs a little help. His computer is substituting the numbers *1* to *13* for some letters. Replace each number in his journal with the letter that spells the word. Then check the bottom of page 13.

JACK'S JOURNAL:

We the peo2le of the United States, in orde12 to form 1 more 3erfect Union, establish justice, insure domestic tranquility, 9rovide for the common defen13e, promote the gener11l welfare, and secure the b4essings of lib10rty to ourselves and our posterity, do ordain and establish this Co7stitution for the

Unite8 St6tes of Am5rica.

Did you fix the words in Jack's journal? Write the letters you used in the spaces with the same numbers here.

a p p l e   a n d   p e a r s
1 2 3 4 5   6 7 8   9 10 11 12 13

Now turn to page 29. Write these code words on Cliff's sign.

Over and Dover

Cy is eager to see the Old Dover Historic District, so Cara points the van toward Dover's downtown area. Soon everyone can see the magnificent old buildings that have stood here for more than 200 years. One of the most famous is the State House Museum. Once Delaware's capitol building, it was built between 1787 and 1792 and served as the government center until 1933. It is now a museum.

While the crew tours the building, you can take a "tour" of your Delaware map. Circle the letter of the correct answer for each question. When you finish, be sure to make a stop at the bottom of page 15.

Don't Forget Your Map!
All the information you need
is on your Delaware map.

1. Which of these is Delaware's largest body of fresh water?

   l. Lake Lewes   **m. Lums Pond**
        n. Rodney Reservoir

2. What is the Delaware state insect?

   a. the monarch butterfly
i. the firefly   **o. the ladybug**

3. Which was never a name of a Delaware settlement?

  r. New Sweden   **s. New Switzerland**
      t. New Netherlands

4. How far have Punkin' Chunkin' teams' machines chunked pumpkins?

s. 100 yards   **t. ³⁄₄ mile**
y. 10 kilometers

7. Which of these cities is farthest from Wilmington?

f. Seaford   **m. Newark**
p. Dover

5. Which Native American people settled in the Delaware area?

q. the Lakota Sioux
s. the Leni-Lenape   **t. the Arapaho**

8. What is the Delaware state song?

d. "My Old Dover Home"
e. "Hail, Delaware"   **t. "Our Delaware"**

6. Which state does *not* border Delaware?

a. New Jersey   **o. Virginia**
u. Pennsylvania

Did you answer all the questions? Now write the letters you circled in the spaces below to form two words.

m o s t   s o f t
1 2 3 4   5 6 7 8

Turn to page 29. Write these two words on Cy Clopedia's sign.

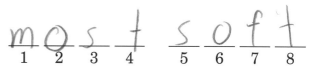

BiG DoiNGS

The crew piles into the Which Way wheels and leaves Dover. Cara drives to Dover Air Force Base. On display here are some of the largest planes in the world, including the C-45, the C-47, and the C-54. However, the biggest of all is the C-5 Galaxy. One of the largest cargo planes in the Western world, the C-5 Galaxy is nearly as long as a football field. The plane can carry many tons of equipment—such as tanks, trucks, and other supplies—anywhere in the world.

The crew is very impressed, but Cy is never at a loss for words. "It's mammoth! Huge! Gigantic!" he shouts. While Cy tries to find words to describe the C-5 Galaxy, you must, too. Find the words that mean *large* in the grid on page 17. It will take a great effort to find them. Look up, down, backward, forward, and diagonally. When you find them all, go to the bottom of the page. A sizeable clue is waiting there.

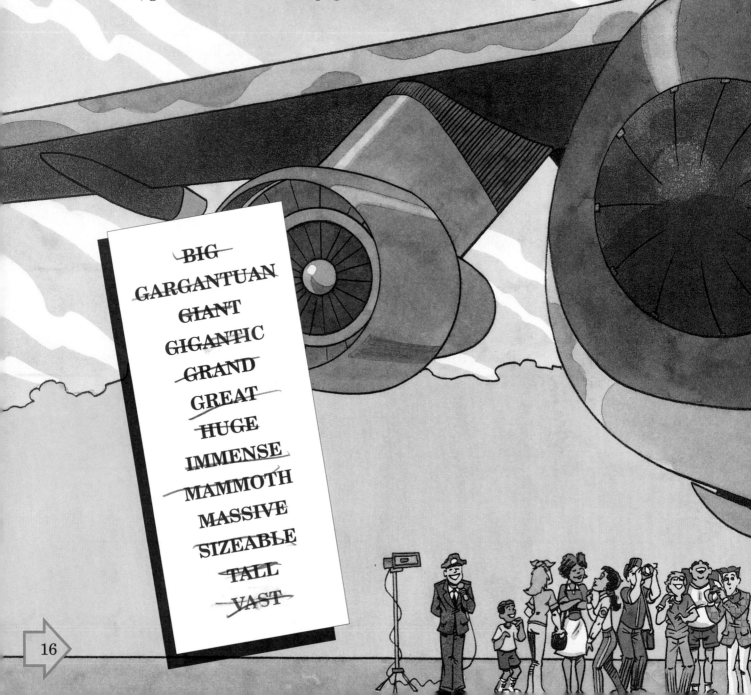

BIG
GARGANTUAN
GIANT
GIGANTIC
GRAND
GREAT
HUGE
IMMENSE
MAMMOTH
MASSIVE
SIZEABLE
TALL
VAST

G C E L B A E Z I S
M A M M O T H G A R
A S R S I G R N C M
E S H G O E U I L A
S G D H A A T V E S
N D U T B N E S T S
E N T H A L T E A I
M A R G D L R U Y V
M R I O N A I T A E
I G I A N T G I B N

Did you find all the BIG words? There are some leftover letters. Write them, in order from left to right and top to bottom, in the spaces below.

cara's sign should have "better dry" on it.

Now go to page 29 and write these words where the instructions tell you.

Splat!

Cara turns the Which Way wheels south again. In the town of Millsboro, Cliff spots signs for the World Championship Punkin' Chunkin'. People gather once a year to see how far they can toss a pumpkin. Some people build very elaborate machines to "chunk" the pumpkins. These contraptions look a lot like giant slingshots, catapults, and cannons.

At one Delaware farm, Cy joins a group of young punkin' chunkers. They're talking about their longest chunks, but they are speaking in number-crankin' code. Instead of telling how many yards long their throws were, they're describing number computations. Cy figures there's a clue here. Help him calculate whose number is the greatest. Then take a measured step down to the bottom of page 19.

RALPH
"To get the number for my first pumpkin, multiply the number of inches in a yard by the number of feet in a yard."

108

JOANIE
"You have to subtract numbers to get my best throw. It's the number of inches in 10 yards minus the number of feet in 10 yards."

330

HERB
"My machine's number is the product of the number of inches in 4 feet and the number of inches in 1 foot."

576

DEBBIE
"To get the number of my best chunk, add the number of inches in 10 yards and the number of inches in 10 feet."

480

HINT:
12 inches = 1 foot
36 inches = 1 yard
3 feet = 1 yard

Did you figure out whose
number is the greatest?

If it is Ralph, the clue is THAT HAT.
If it is Joanie, the clue is FAST BUS.
If it is Herb, the clue is PARK CAR.
If it is Debbie, the clue is TINY BUG.

Now write the clue words on
Jack and Jill's sign on page 29.

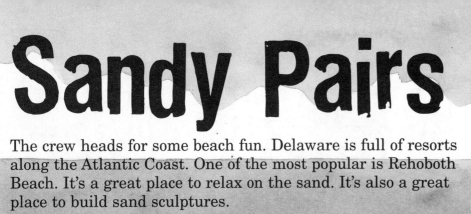

Sandy Pairs

The crew heads for some beach fun. Delaware is full of resorts along the Atlantic Coast. One of the most popular is Rehoboth Beach. It's a great place to relax on the sand. It's also a great place to build sand sculptures.

There's a sand-sculpture contest going on when the crew arrives. Cara and Jill watch the artists build their sandy creations. Cliff snaps pictures of some of his favorite contest entries. Although he thought he took pictures of finished sculptures, some artists changed their sand structures just a bit. Find how many sand sculptures match Cliff's photos. Then dig up your next clue on the bottom of page 21.

How many sand sculptures matched Cliff's snapshots?

If two matched, cross off the CHURCH.

If three matched, cross off the PLANTATION.

If four matched, cross off the MILL.

Now turn to page 30 and cross off your first famous place.

PRETTY PETS

Back on the road and heading northwest, Cy hears some lively merry-go-round music in the distance as they pass Harrington. He's not hearing things—it's the Delaware State Fair in full swing. The crew wants to go to the fair, so Cara heads toward the fairgrounds.

The twins are soon nose-deep in cotton candy. Cliff and Cara check out the rides. Cy spies the animal tent and heads that way. Inside the animal barn, there's a wacky competition going on. It's the Pretty Animals Contest. People from around the state dress their pets in wild costumes. There are prizes for the best-looking animals.

Cy comes in just as the awards are being announced. Help him figure out who won first, second, and third place. When you've got it all figured out, go to the bottom of page 23.

CLUES

1. The first-place winner wore sunglasses and footwear.

2. An animal without a hat won second place.

3. The third-place winner doesn't have four legs.

4. The animals wearing pink or blue didn't win anything.

Did you help Cy discover the winners? Each animal has a two-letter clue near it. Write each clue, in order of first, second, and third place, in the spaces below.

M U S C U M

Now go to page 30 and cross off this place.

TRAPPED!

Cliff wants to get out and explore some wilderness areas. The crew decides to drive south on Route 13 to Trap Pond State Park. The pond was created in the late 1700s when colonists cut down many cedar trees in the heart of the swamp. It became one of Delaware's first state parks in 1951. Its freshwater wetlands are great for canoeing. Soon the crew members are gliding among dozens of bald cypress trees. They hope to catch a glimpse of some of the park's wildlife.

The twins are so busy looking for animals that they fall behind. Soon they're completely lost! Help them find their way back through the trees to the rest of the crew. When you do, paddle down to the bottom of page 25.

START

T

A

P

M

L

N

P

A

R

W

D

Did you get the twins back to the rest of the crew?
There were letters along the correct path. Write them,
in order from *last* to *first*, in the spaces below.

p l a n t a t i o n

Now cross off this Delaware landmark on page 30.

See you, Caesar!

Rooms to spare

Right Light

CROSS OFF THE STATE PARK AND THE CANAL.

Your Which Way Delaware adventure is almost over. Your final stop is Fenwick Island off the southern coast of the state. Fenwick Lighthouse was built in 1858 to guide ships past the Delaware shores. Visitors to the island can see the lighthouse. Not too many people live on the island. It still looks much like it did when the first explorers discovered the area almost 400 years ago.

As the sun sets behind the lighthouse, your thoughts travel to all the places you've seen in Delaware. Travel the final Which Way puzzle to get your last clue. Place a penny or other marker on START. Answer the first question and move your counter forward the correct number of spaces. Answer the other questions and keep moving forward. The space you finish on will give you your final clue. Then go to the bottom of page 27.

Don't Forget Your Map!
Use your map of Delaware to answer
all the questions.

Almost home?

CROSS OFF THE CANAL AND THE MILLS.

Canoe for two

Sand van

Park art

CROSS OFF THE MUSEUM
AND THE MILLS.

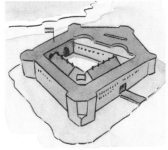

Pea Patch Place

1. What is the state fish of Delaware?

   a. Strongarm catfish (move one square)
   b. Weakfish (move two squares)
   c. Delaware lake trout (move three squares)

2. What is the Delaware town with the third-largest population?

   a. Dover (move two squares)
   b. Wilmington (move four squares)
   c. Newark (move six squares)

3. Nylon was invented in what year?

   a. 1935 (move one square)
   b. 1953 (move three squares)
   c. 1835 (move five squares)

4. How much does the clam in the Delaware Museum of Natural History weigh?

   a. 400 pounds (move three squares)
   b. 500 pounds (move four squares)
   c. 50 pounds (move five squares)

Enormous!

CROSS OFF THE
PLANTATION
AND THE CANAL.

Have you reached the final square on the game board? Look at the two places listed in that box. You can cross them off on page 30.

CROSS OFF THE MILLS
AND THE STATE PARK.

See tweets

UFO or UFP?

Who?

Which famous person from Delaware is going to the Which Way Hall of Fame? Solve the puzzles on pages 2 through 11. Each puzzle will help you eliminate one candidate. When there is only one person left, you will have your answer!

Éleuthère Irénée du Pont
Frenchman whose Delaware gunpowder mill became the chemical giant the DuPont Company

Mary Ann Shadd Cary
Founder of the *Provincial Freeman* and the first black woman in North America to become a newspaper editor

Annie Jump Cannon
Astronomer nicknamed the "Census Taker of the Skies"

Howard Pyle
Illustrator and writer of children's books who opened an art school in Wilmington

Richard Allen
Former slave who founded the African Methodist Episcopal Church, the first black church in the country

Caesar Rodney
Signer of the Declaration of Independence and governor of Delaware from 1778 to 1781

The person going into the Hall of Fame is: ➡️ Éleuthere Irénée du pont

What?

One item from Delaware will go into the Which Way museum. To find out what it is, solve the puzzles on pages 12 through 19. Each puzzle will give you some code words. Write the code words on the correct signs. Then write the letters in the box at the bottom of the page to crack the code.

apple and pears
1 2 3 4 5 6 7 8 9 10 11 12 13

most soft
14 15 16 17 18 19 20 21

better dry
22 23 24 25 26 27 28 29 30

park car
31 32 33 34 35 36 37

The item going into the Which Way Museum is:

A b a l d e y p r e s s t r e e f r o M
1 22 6 4 28 35 30 31 29 23 18 13 17 33 10 26 20 27 19 14

t r a p p o n d s t a t e p a r k
21 37 36 2 3 15 7 8 16 24 32 25 5 9 11 12 34

Where?

One landmark from Delaware is to be featured in the Which Way Supermax Movie. To find out where the Which Way cameras are going, solve the puzzles on pages 20 through 27. Each puzzle will help you cross off one or more of the famous places. When you finish, the remaining landmark will be the answer.

✗Old Swedes Church
Founded in 1698, one of the oldest churches in America

Cape Henlopen State Park
Created in 1682, one of the nation's first public parks

✗ Eleutherian Mills
Mansion site of Éleuthère Irénée du Pont and part of the 240-acre Hagley Museum

✗ Chesapeake & Delaware Canal
Open in 1829, enabling cargo ships to travel from the Chesapeake Bay to the Delaware River

✗ Zwaanendael Museum
Historical museum in Lewes built to look like an old Dutch town hall

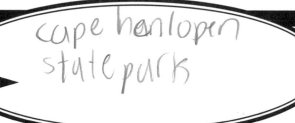

✗ John Dickinson Plantation
Restored colonial home of statesman who was called the "penman of the Revolution"

The famous place is:

cape henlopen state park

All the answers for your
Which Way adventure
are on the next two
pages. Do not go

unless you need help
with a puzzle. If you
don't need help,

before you look at
the answers.

You can use the rest of
this page to work out
your puzzles. If you need
a little extra space,

your pencil here. After
you're done, make a

back to the page you
were working on.

ANSWERS

Pages 2-3: Statue Stop

1. ZWAANENDAEL
2. CONSTITUTION
3. A LIGHTHOUSE
4. GUNPOWDER
5. PEA PATCH ISLAND
6. JAMES BRANCH
7. HMB *DE BRAAK*

The leftover letters spell CHURCH FOUNDER. Delete Richard Allen from page 28.

Pages 4-5: Parlor Puzzle
The message reads

I T   I S   N O T   T H E

A S T R O N O M E R.

This eliminates Annie Jump Cannon from page 28.

Pages 6-7: Seeing Doubles

The skate is hidden only once. Cross off the Declaration signer, Caesar Rodney, on page 28.

Pages 8-9: Pass the Ps

1. P I P (E) R
2. P I (L) L O W
3. P U P P (Y)
4. P U R (P) L E
5. P U D (D) L E
6. P E R (R) F U M E
7. P I A N O
8. P O W W O (W)
9. P O (T) A T O
10. P I T (C) H E R

Written from last to first, the circled letters spell HOWARD PYLE. Cross him off on page 28.

Pages 10-11: Day in Bombay

B								
O			H		D			M
S	T	D	L	U	M	U	D	A
T	H	E	E	D	I	T	O	R
O	R	L	W	S	L	C	V	Y
N	E	M	E	O	K	H	E	D
	E	A	S	N		R	E	
		R						L

The letters in the shaded boxes spell THE EDITOR. Cross Mary Ann Shadd Cary off the list on page 28.

Pages 12-13: Square Words
We the peo**P**le of the United States, in orde**R** to form **A** more **P**erfect Union, establish justice, insure domestic tranquility, **P**rovide for the common defen**S**e, promote the gener**A**l welfare, and secure the b**L**essings of lib**E**rty to ourselves and our posterity, do ordain and establish this Co**N**stitution for the Unite**D** St**A**tes of Am**E**rica.

The correct letters spell

A P P L E   A N D   P E A R S.
1 2 3 4 5   6 7 8   9 10 11 12 13

Write these words on Cliff's sign on page 29.

Pages 14-15: Over and Dover
1. **m** 2. **o** 3. **s** 4. **t** 5. **s** 6. **o** 7. **f** 8. **t**
The code words for Cy's sign on page 29 are MOST SOFT.